E
FRI

Frisky, Margaret

Mystery of the magic
meadow

C2

DATE		
MAY 15 '73		
JUL 30 '73		
NOV 21		

© THE BAKER & TAYLOR CO.

MYSTERY OF THE
MAGIC MEADOW

By Margaret Friskey

Illustrations by Frances Eckart

CHILDRENS PRESS, CHICAGO

Library of Congress Catalog Card Number: 68-12826

2 3 4 5 6 7 8 9 10 11 12 13 14 15 16 17 18 19 20 21 22 23 24 25   R   75 74 73 72 71 70 69

Hush and Shush were
two little rabbits.
    They lived under a bush
near a field of clover.

They did not make a sound
as they hopped across the field.
They were quiet as shadows
on the grass. They saw

a frog on a log,

a fat groundhog,

two squirrels in a tree

and three chipmunks.

A third little rabbit
lived under the bush.
 He was a NOISY one!
 He stepped on sticks.
 He sent stones rolling.
Snap! Crash! Rattle! He
hopped across the field.

 His name was Rackety.
 All the animals in the field
disappeared when they heard him.

"We have the whole field
for ourselves," said Rackety
one day.

"No we don't," said Hush.
"Be quiet and you can see
who lives with us," said Shush.

The next day Rackety
watched his feet. He put them
down, one after the other.

He was quiet as a feather
on a breeze . . . . . . until
he fell into the stream.
Plop!

He shook one hind foot
and then the other.
He looked all around.
"Nobody lives in our field
but us rabbits," said Rackety.

Then one hot day Rackety
stopped to rest. He was quiet
as the cotton in a quilt.
    That is when he saw the
frog on a log.

He ran all the way home.

"A frog lives over there,"
he said. "HE catches flies
with his long tongue."

"That is his way," said Hush.

"And he sleeps in the mud
in the bottom of the stream,"
said Rackety.

"That is his way," said Shush.

One day Rackety said, "Nobody
lives in this field but us rabbits
and one frog on a log."
That is when he stepped
in a hole and rolled over.
The fat groundhog popped up
and scolded him.

Rackety ran all the way home.
"There is a fat groundhog,"
he shouted. "HE lives in a hole
in the ground."
"That is his way," said Hush.

The summer days went by.
"Nobody lives in our field,"
said Rackety, "but us rabbits,
one frog on a log,
and a fat groundhog."
That is when a squirrel
dropped a nut on his head.

"There are two silly squirrels,"
said Rackety. "THEY take nuts
up into an old elm tree."
    "That is their way,"
said Shush.

The summer days went by.
"Nobody lives in our field,"
said Rackety, "but us rabbits,
one frog on a log,
one fat groundhog,
and two squirrels in a tree."
That is when he saw the
chipmunks.

Rackety ran all the way home.
"There are three of them,"
said Rackety. "And those chipmunks
live in tunnels under the ground."
"That is their way," said Hush.

Then one day a large creature
walked into the field. She sat
down in the middle of it. She
drew a picture of the field on a
big white paper. She was quiet
as the sunshine on her hat.

All the animals came to watch
her. They forgot about each other.
The creature laughed when she
saw them all living in the field.
She put them all in her picture.
The three rabbits,
the frog on a log,
the fat groundhog,
the two squirrels in a tree
and three chipmunks.

Then she picked up her
picture and went away.
    She left the field to the
animals that lived there,
each in his own way.

Rackety hopped
across the field,
happy as could be.
   He sent a stone
bouncing through the clover.
   He said, so anyone
could hear him, "NOBODY
lives in this field
but us rabbits,
      a frog on a log,
       a fat groundhog,
         two squirrels in a tree
            and three chipmunks,
and that is as it should be."